# CONTENTS

CW00942261

# CHARACTER LIST

**NARRATOR(S)**  This role can either be taken by an adult or shared between two or three children. Please note that the narrator or narrators need to have strong, clear speaking voices.

**EMPEROR**  Has a small speaking part and would suit a child with confidence and an air of authority!

**TOWNSPEOPLE**  Non-speaking. Have as many as you like to create the 'hustle bustle' of the first scene. They become the choir once they exit the stage.

**THE CURIOUS SHEEP**  The central character; sings a solo; largish speaking part; needs a removable woolly costume!

**SHEEP**  Have as many as you like. Two have small speaking parts and they all perform a simple dance with the shepherds in song 5.

**SHEPHERD(S)**  Have as many as you like. Three have small speaking parts and all perform a simple dance with the sheep in song 5.

**MARY**  Non-speaking part.

**JOSEPH**  Non-speaking part.

**DONKEY**  Non-speaking part.

**BALTHASAR**  Small speaking part.

**MELCHIOR**  Small speaking part.

**CASPAR**  Small speaking part.

**ANGELS**  Have as many as you like dressed as gospel singers, with wings. One has a small speaking part.

**BABY JESUS**  Don't forget the main character - a good-sized doll that can be rocked convincingly!

# A note on stage directions

Suggestions for stage directions are provided throughout the script, but please note that these are meant as guidelines only. We suggest that once the shepherds and sheep are on stage they remain there for the majority of the play whilst all the other action goes on around them or infront of them, as indicated in the script. When it is time for the shepherds and the Curious Sheep to make their way to Bethlehem, all the sheep should exit the stage so that the stable scene can be set up.

# SCRIPT

*The townspeople stand in a crowd chatting to each other noisily. As the Emperor enters, the townspeople hush each other and everyone immediately goes quiet as they look at the Emporer, who holds his head high and looks very important.*

**NARRATOR**    Two thousand years ago the Roman Emperor Caesar Augustus made a very big decision.

**EMPEROR**    *(In a loud voice)* I have decided to conduct a census. All the people in my empire should return to the place where they were born so that their names can be recorded.

*Emperor exits the stage.*

**NARRATOR**    Very soon across the land of Judea the streets were filled with the hustle bustle of people getting ready for their journeys.

*During the following song the townspeople act out the preparations for a long journey: loading carts, packing possessions and setting out.*

**Song 1.    HUSTLE BUSTLE**    CD track 1/8

*After the song, the townspeople exit the stage and sit at the side to become the choir. The shepherds and sheep enter. The sheep lie down and graze.*

**NARRATOR**    But not everyone was rushing about. As night fell on a hilltop just outside Nazareth, some shepherds were watching their flock grazing quietly in the twilight. Although it was late, the smallest, youngest sheep just could not settle down. She could sense that something was going on and she was feeling rather curious.

**Song 2.    SOMETHING'S GOING ON**    CD track 2/9
*(The flock of sheep should get more and more irritated with the Curious Sheep as she goes on throughout the song)*

**NARRATOR**    Eventually the Curious Sheep managed to settle down, but just as she was starting to feel drowsy, she noticed a man leading a donkey on the road far beneath her.

*Mary, Joseph and the donkey walk slowly backwards and forwards in front of the stage in view of the Curious Sheep.*

**CURIOUS SHEEP**    Now that really is curious! I wonder where they are going so late at night.

**NARRATOR**    The donkey looked tired and the Curious Sheep could just make out the shape of a young woman sitting on the donkey's back.

**CURIOUS SHEEP**    They all look exhausted. I'm sure the others will be interested to see this.

| | |
|---|---|
| **NARRATOR** | But the other sheep were all snoring loudly now *(they snore)* and she thought she'd better not wake them. So the Curious Sheep went back to lie down and watched the couple and their donkey as they made their way along the road far below. |
| **CURIOUS SHEEP** | *(Fidgeting excitedly)* From up here I can see the whole world. There's so much to look at and so much to do. I just can't keep still. |

*Mary, Joseph and the donkey stop for a rest at the side of the stage. The sheep yawn and they start to snore even louder than before.*

| | |
|---|---|
| **NARRATOR** | *(Shouting over the sheep's snoring)* To her the world was new and everything was exciting. But the rest of her flock were tired after a long day grazing. |
| **SHEEP 1** | *(To the narrator, crossly)* Can you please be quiet? Some of us are trying to get some rest! *(The snoring stops)* |
| **NARRATOR** | *(In a whisper)* Sorry! |
| **CURIOUS SHEEP** | But I can't go to sleep! What if something exciting happens while my eyes are shut? |
| **SHEEP 2** | *(Irritated)* Nothing is going to happen. Nothing ever happens around here. We eat grass and we sleep. That's what sheep do! |
| **CURIOUS SHEEP** | No! Something exciting is going to happen, I can tell. And I don't want to be snoring when it does! |
| **WHOLE FLOCK** | Just be quiet! |

*The Curious Sheep looks dejected and sad.*

| | |
|---|---|
| **CURIOUS SHEEP** | It's no good – I know something exciting is going to happen. I can feel it in my tummy. |

*The following song is sung by the choir and by Mary, Joseph and the donkey, who again start to walk backwards and forwards wearily in front of the stage. With each verse they get slower and more weary. The sheep and shepherds doze, all except for the Curious Sheep who looks on, still fidgeting excitedly.*

**Song 3.   HOW MUCH FURTHER TO BETHLEHEM?**      **CD track 3/10**

*Mary, Joseph and the donkey disappear from view.*

| | |
|---|---|
| **NARRATOR** | As the donkey disappeared over the horizon, the Curious Sheep shut her eyes and tried to get to sleep. |
| **CURIOUS SHEEP** | I'm trying my hardest, but it's so difficult! I'm still too excited! |

*The Three Wise Men enter, set out a map on the ground and crowd round it, scratching their heads.*

| | |
|---|---|
| **NARRATOR** | Meanwhile, a few miles away, three wise men were scratching their heads and puzzling over the map they had set out on the ground. |
| **MELCHIOR** | The prophesies tell of a new king, but we have been searching for many days. My calculations show we are close, but which direction should we go in now? |
| **BALTHASAR** | I'm not sure, Melchior. I have studied my charts closely, but still the path is not clear to me. What do you think Caspar? |
| **CASPAR** | *(Turning the map round)* I think we have the map the wrong way up. We should have turned left at Jericho! |
| **NARRATOR** | As they pondered what to do, a dazzling star suddenly appeared in the Eastern sky. It lit up the hills and fields all around them. The three wise men turned from their map and stared up in wonder. |
| **MELCHIOR** | It is the brightest star I have ever seen. What does it mean? |
| **CASPAR** | It is so beautiful. Surely this is the sign that we have been waiting for. What do you think we should do, Balthasar? |
| **BALTHASAR** | We must follow it and see where it leads. |

**Song 4.   CALYPSO KINGS**                                    CD track 4/11

*The Three Wise Men exit the stage.*

| | |
|---|---|
| **NARRATOR** | But it wasn't just the wise men who were watching the bright star. Back in her field the Curious Sheep had noticed it too and so had the shepherds and their flock. *(Sheep start to run around the stage in a frightened manner)* Startled by the sudden light, the sheep started to race around the field in fear and excitement. The shepherds did their best to round them all up. |

**Song 5.   HEY EWE!**                                    CD track 5/12

*During this song the shepherds and the sheep could perform a simple dance. The sheep could be divided into groups of four, linking arms for the first line of each verse; running forward a little and then back a little for 'Run up the hill, run down again'; making a circle and skipping round for 'Round and round they run about'; raising their arms in the air for 'Till they hear the shepherds shout'. The sheep could then hold hands and skip round in their groups of four during the chorus, with one sheep from each group leaving the stage at the end of each chorus so that by the last verse, only one sheep is left in each group dancing about on their own. Some simple choreography for the shepherds during the choruses could be very effective.*

| | |
|---|---|
| **NARRATOR** | When all the sheep had been rounded up, the shepherds settled down for a well-earned rest and soon everyone was asleep and snoring softly… but not for long! |

*The angels appear dressed as a gospel choir, with wings.*

| | |
|---|---|
| **ANGEL 1** | *(Spreading out his/her arms)* Listen to me! I am an angel of God and I bring you good news of great joy. This night a baby will be born in Bethlehem. You must go and worship Him. |

**Song 6.    GOSPEL ANGELS**                                    CD track 6/13

*(Have fun choreographing simple dance movements for the angels, alongside the clapping and the backing vocals)*

| | |
|---|---|
| **SHEPHERD 1** | But Bethlehem is a big city. How will we find Him? |
| **ANGEL 1** | Just follow the star and you will find Him lying in a manger in a stable. |
| **NARRATOR** | The shepherds were nervous about what they had heard. But they were also excited, so they decided to set out immediately for Bethlehem. |

*Shepherds pick up their crooks and leave for Bethlehem, walking towards the front of the stage.*

| | |
|---|---|
| **CURIOUS SHEEP** | Now I am sure something curious is happening! I must find out what it is! |
| **NARRATOR** | So the Curious Sheep started running after the shepherds as quickly as she could. |
| **SHEPHERD 2** | *(Looking back)* Looks like this little lady doesn't want to be left behind. |
| **SHEPHERD 3** | Let's take her with us. |
| **NARRATOR** | So the shepherds set off for Bethlehem taking the Curious Sheep with them. |

*The shepherds and the Curious Sheep exit to the right of the stage and the rest of the sheep exit to the left of the stage. The manger is brought on to the stage and Mary and Joseph stand, gazing at the baby lying in the manger. The wise men, shepherds and the Curious Sheep make their way to the stable by walking in front of the stage and entering the stable, stage left.*

| | |
|---|---|
| **NARRATOR** | When they reached the stable they could see a man and his wife gazing fondly at a baby lying in the manger. The shepherds and the wise men crowded round, but the Curious Sheep couldn't see what was going on. |
| **MELCHIOR** | The prophesies were right, for surely we have found the Son of God. |
| **CASPAR** | We come bearing gifts. |

*The Three Wise Men lay their gifts at the foot of the manger.*

| | |
|---|---|
| **BALTHASAR** | I bring you gold. |
| **MELCHIOR** | I bring you frankincense. |
| **CASPAR** | And I bring you myrrh. |

*Mary smiles, picks up the baby from the crib and holds Him in her arms, rocking Him gently.*

| NARRATOR | The Curious Sheep pushed her way to the front so that she could get a better look. |
|---|---|
| CURIOUS SHEEP | What strange gifts to give to a baby! |
| NARRATOR | The Curious Sheep noticed that the baby's crib was hard and uncomfortable. |
| CURIOUS SHEEP | I know, I will give Him my fleece to lie on. |

*The Curious Sheep removes her fleece and lays it in the manger. Mary puts the baby back in the crib and she and Joseph gaze fondly at Him again.*

| NARRATOR | So she gave the baby her fleece and the Curious Sheep felt proud to have given Him such a useful present. |
|---|---|
| CURIOUS SHEEP | All these people worshipping such a tiny baby. Now that really is curious! |

**Song 7.    A KING IS BORN**                              **CD track 7/14**

# THE END!

# Hustle Bustle

Words and Music by
Antony Copus

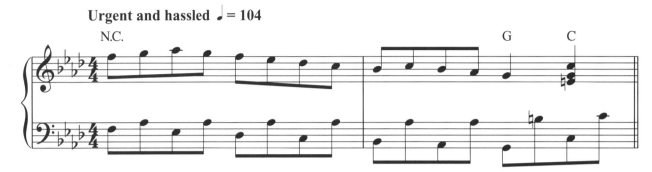

Hus - tle bus - tle, let's get bu - sy, plan - ning for our jour - ney.

Hus - tle bus - tle, let's get bu - sy, must be on our way.

all a-cross the land we must tra-vel to the place of our birth.

birth.

**Rush to the end**

Hus - tle bus - tle, let's get bu - sy, hus - tle bus - tle, let's get bu - sy,

hus - tle bus - tle, must be on our way.

# Something's Going On

Words and Music by
Antony Copus

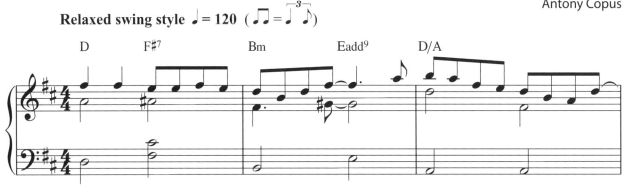

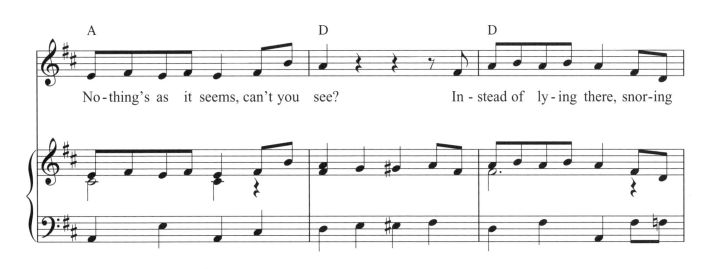

in the eve - ning air,       why don't you help me solve this mys - te -

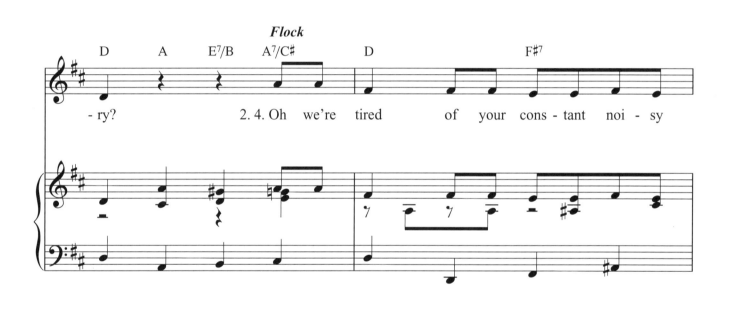

*Flock*

- ry?       2. 4. Oh we're tired      of your cons - tant noi - sy

bleat - ing.       No - thing's go - ing on,   can't you see?       So just

go to sleep_ you noi-sy sheep, and for-get a-bout your mys - te - ry.

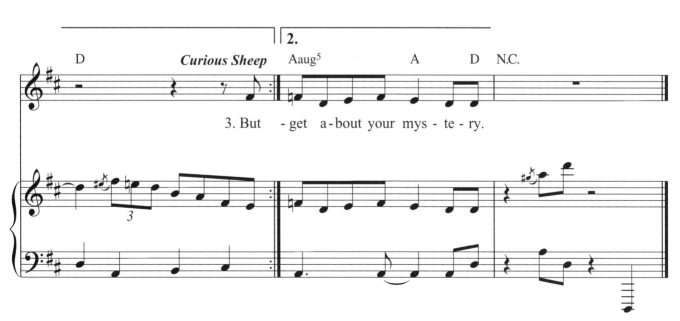

*Curious Sheep*

3. But - get a-bout your mys - te - ry.

# How Much Further To Bethlehem?

Words and Music by
Antony Copus

feet are feel-ing ev - er so tired.___ But with a smile and a song___ we

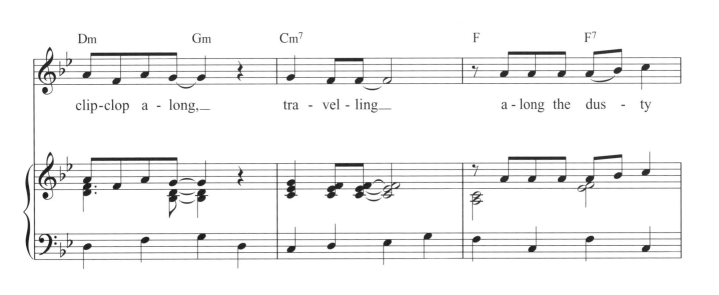

clip-clop a - long,___ tra - vel - ling___ a - long the dus - ty

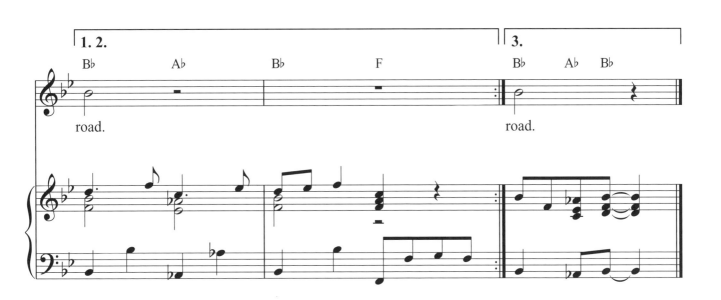

road.

road.

15

# Calypso Kings

Words and Music by
Antony Copus

**Calypso style** ♩ = 144

1. We must fol-low the star to Beth - le - hem___ to find the new - born King.___ We must fol-low the star to Beth - le - hem,___ for Him our pre - sents we bring.

# Hey Ewe!

Words and Music by
Antony Copus

19

# Gospel Angels

Words and Music by
Antony Copus

tra-vel to the town of Beth-le-hem and search for the new-born King. Sing

Glo-ry to God in the high-est, give thanks for the peace He brings. So

Baa baa baa baa Baa baa baa

*To Coda* ⊕ **1.**

sing your praise to Him, the new-born King!

*D.%̸ al Coda*

✛ **CODA**

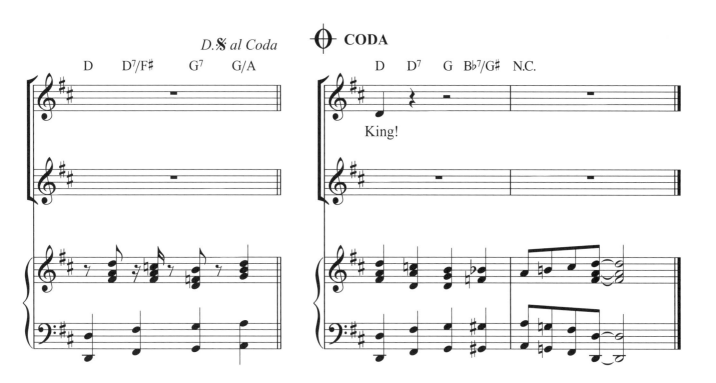

King!

# A King Is Born

Words and Music by
Antony Copus

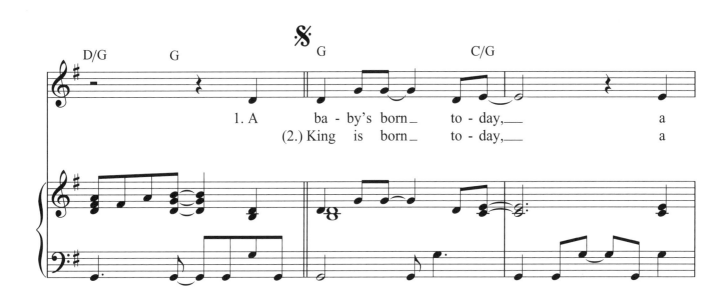

1. A ba - by's born_ to - day,_ a
(2.) King is born_ to - day,_ a

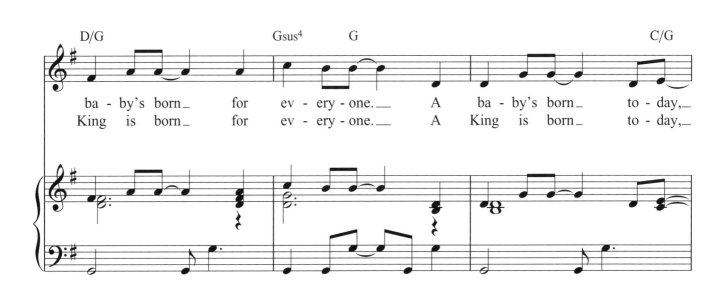

ba - by's born_ for ev - ery - one._ A ba - by's born_ to - day,_
King is born_ for ev - ery - one._ A King is born_ to - day,_

a ba - by's born__ to save us all.__
a King is born__ to save us all.__

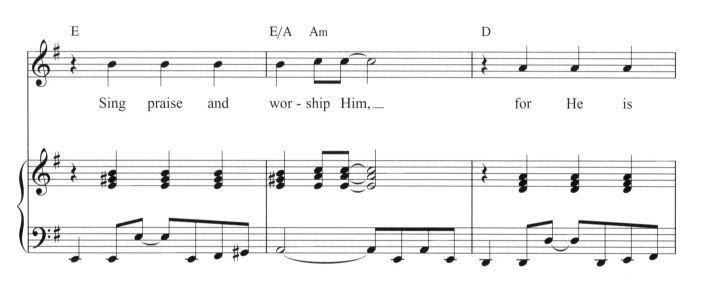

Sing praise and wor - ship Him,__ for He is

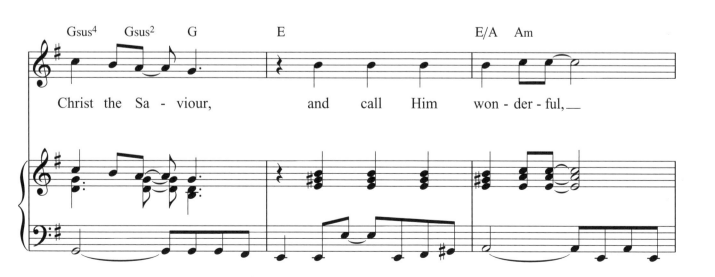

Christ the Sa - viour, and call Him won - der - ful,__

25

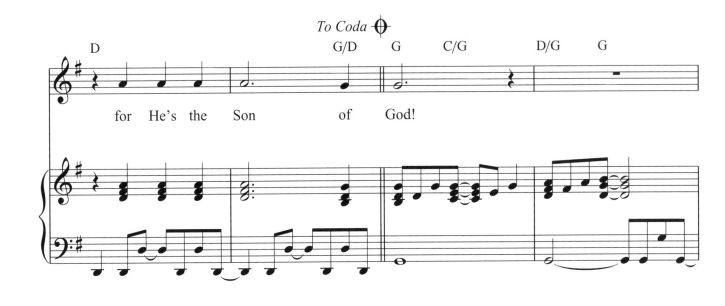

for He's the Son of God!

2. A

God!

26

# Hustle Bustle

**CHORUS**     *Hustle bustle, let's get busy,*
*Planning for our journey.*
*Hustle bustle, let's get busy,*
*Must be on our way.*
*(Repeat)*

1    Caesar has decreed a law we all must heed:
We must travel to the place of our birth.
Just as Caesar planned, all across the land
We must travel to the place of our birth.

**CHORUS**

*Repeat verse*

**CHORUS**     *Hustle bustle, let's get busy,*
*Hustle bustle, let's get busy,*
*Hustle bustle, must be on our way.*

Words and Music by Antony Copus
© 2012 Out of the Ark Ltd, Middlesex TW12 2HD
CCLI Song No. 6150949

# Something's Going On

**Curious Sheep (solo)**

1   Something's going on I just know it.
    Nothing's as it seems, can't you see?
    Instead of lying there, snoring in the evening air,
    Why don't you help me solve this mystery?

2   **Flock**

    Oh we're tired of your constant noisy bleating.
    Nothing's going on, can't you see?
    So just go to sleep you noisy sheep,
    And forget about your mystery.

3   **Curious Sheep**

    But something's going on I just know it.
    Nothing's as it seems, can't you see?
    Instead of lying there, snoring in the evening air,
    Why don't you help me solve this mystery?

4   **Flock**

    Oh we're tired of your constant noisy bleating.
    Nothing's going on, can't you see?
    So just go to sleep you noisy sheep,
    And forget about your mystery.

Words and Music by Antony Copus
© 2012 Out of the Ark Ltd, Middlesex TW12 2HD
CCLI Song No. 6150956

# How Much Further To Bethlehem?

1   How much further to Bethlehem?
    It feels like we've been walking for hours.
    How much further to Bethlehem?
    Our feet are feeling ever so tired.
    But with a smile and a song we clip-clop along,
    Travelling along the dusty road.

2   How much further to Bethlehem?
    It feels like we've been walking for miles.
    How much further to Bethlehem?
    Our feet are feeling ever so tired.
    But with a smile and a song we clip-clop along,
    Travelling along the dusty road.

3   How much further to Bethlehem?
    It feels like we've been walking for hours.
    How much further to Bethlehem?
    Our feet are feeling ever so tired.
    But with a smile and a song we clip-clop along,
    Travelling along the dusty road.

Words and Music by Antony Copus
© 2012 Out of the Ark Ltd, Middlesex TW12 2HD
CCLI Song No. 6150970

# Calypso Kings

1   We must follow the star to Bethlehem
To find the newborn King.
We must follow the star to Bethlehem,
For Him our presents we bring.

**CHORUS**   *Follow the star, follow the star,*
*Follow the star to Bethlehem.*
*Follow the star, follow the star,*
*Follow the star to Him.*

*Repeat verse*

**CHORUS x 2**

Words and Music by Antony Copus
© 2012 Out of the Ark Ltd, Middlesex TW12 2HD
CCLI Song No. 6150987

# Hey Ewe!

1   Four worried sheep escape from the pen,
    Run up the hill, run down again.
    Round and round they run about
    Till they hear the shepherds shout:

> ***Shepherds***
>
> **CHORUS** *Hey ewe! Come back here,*
> *Everything's gonna be alright.*
> *Hey ewe! Come back here,*
> *Or we're gonna be here all night!*
> *Hey ewe!*

2   Three worried sheep escape from the pen,
    Run up the hill, run down again.
    Round and round they run about
    Till they hear the shepherds shout:

**CHORUS**

3   Two worried sheep escape from the pen,
    Run up the hill, run down again.
    Round and round they run about
    Till they hear the shepherds shout:

**CHORUS**

4   One worried sheep escapes from the pen,
    Runs up the hill, runs down again.
    Round and round they run about
    Till they hear the shepherds shout:

**CHORUS**

Words and Music by Antony Copus
© 2012 Out of the Ark Ltd, Middlesex TW12 2HD
CCLI Song No. 6151027

# Gospel Angels

1    Wake up you sleepy shepherds!
      We're angels of the Lord.
      Listen you sleepy shepherds!
      We bring you the word of God.
      So travel to the town of Bethlehem
      And search for the newborn King.
      Sing Glory to God in the highest,
      Give thanks for the peace He brings.
      So sing your praise to Him, the newborn King!
      *Repeat*

*Instrumental*

*Repeat verse*

Words and Music by Antony Copus
© 2012 Out of the Ark Ltd, Middlesex TW12 2HD
CCLI Song No. 6151041

# A King Is Born

1   A baby's born today,
     A baby's born for everyone.
     A baby's born today,
     A baby's born to save us all.

**CHORUS** *Sing praise and worship Him,*
*For He is Christ the Saviour,*
*And call Him wonderful,*
*For He's the Son of God!*

2   A King is born today,
     A King is born for everyone.
     A King is born today,
     A King is born to save us all.

**CHORUS**

Words and Music by Antony Copus
© 2012 Out of the Ark Ltd, Middlesex TW12 2HD
CCLI Song No. 6151058

# COPYRIGHT & LICENSING - What You Need To Know

The world of copyright and licensing can seem very daunting, particularly because there is an obligation on schools to comply with copyright law. We're here to help you through the process and to keep you legal. The guidelines below explain the most common copyright and licensing issues.

## Staging This Musical

Performing this musical to an audience (other than pupils and staff) requires a performance licence.

**\*\* Please note that your Performing Rights Society (PRS) Licence does NOT cover musicals\*\***

We issue affordable performance licences to schools, churches and nurseries. To apply, simply complete the performance licence application form on page 35 and fax or post it to us.

The performance licence will permit the holder to:
- Perform the musical on the dates applied for.
- Reproduce the song lyrics on printed paper, e.g. for programmes, to make transparencies for overhead projection and to display the lyrics on an interactive whiteboard or other type of screen. The following credit should be included with the lyrics:
  *'Reproduced by kind permission © Out of the Ark Ltd'*
- Photocopy the script for learning purposes. Copies must be destroyed after the performance.
- Make up to two photocopies of the music score for use by participating musicians on the performance dates.
- Play the CD (either backing tracks or vocal tracks) at the performance.

## Putting On A Concert

If you are not staging this musical but are performing any of our songs for the public on school premises (i.e. to anyone other than pupils or staff) then royalty payments become due. Contact Out of the Ark Music directly to obtain a licence. **Please note:** There is no need to obtain a licence from the publisher if your school has an arrangement with the **Performing Rights Society (PRS)** either directly or through the local authority.

## Making an Audio Recording or a Video of the Performance

If you wish to make an audio or video recording of your performance of any of our works please visit www.outoftheark.com/licensing for further information.

### Singing Songs in the Classroom

You are free to use all of the material – including songs and scripts – in the classroom for teaching purposes. If photocopying any part of the book for teaching purposes please record this usage on your school's photocopy log to ensure that you are legally protected.

### Singing Songs in an Assembly or in Church

Songs may be sung in assembly without charge. In addition the CD may be played provided that your school has a PRS licence. However, the reproduction of the lyrics and/or musical scores for use in an assembly or a church requires a licence. The following licences from Christian Copyright Licensing Limited (www.ccli.com) permit the photocopying or reproduction of song lyrics or musical scores – for example to create song sheets, overhead transparencies or to display the lyrics or music using any electronic display medium:

        **For UK schools:** A Collective Worship Copyright Licence and a Music Reproduction Licence
        **For churches:** A Church Copyright and Music Reproduction Licence

Please ensure that you log the songs that are used on your CCLI and MRL copy report.

Organisations that do not hold one of the above licences should contact Out of the Ark Limited directly for permission.

Your CCLI licence also grants you permission to display the song lyrics from our Words on Screen™ CD ROMS on a whiteboard or other screen. Simply log the song titles on your copy report.

### Copying and File-sharing

Copying Out of the Ark Music's audio CDs is not permitted without obtaining a licence from the publisher. Installation of Out of the Ark Music's audio CD tracks on to a computer is strictly forbidden without a licence – we can provide schools with a 'Learning Platform Installation Licence'. File-sharing of any of our audio tracks or CD ROM files is strictly prohibited. For more information visit **www.outoftheark.com/licensing**.

---

Helpful information can be found on the following website:

**A Guide to Licensing Copyright in Schools: www.outoftheark.com/licensing**

And remember, we are always happy to help. For advice simply contact our customer services team:

Tel: +44 (0)20 8481 7200
Email: copyright@outoftheark.com

# LICENCE APPLICATION FORM
## (Hey Ewe!)

If you perform **Hey Ewe!** to an audience other than children and staff you will need to photocopy and complete this form and return it by post or fax to Out of the Ark Music in order to apply for a licence. If anticipated audience sizes are very small or if special circumstances apply please contact Out of the Ark Music.

**The licence will permit the holder to:**
- Perform *Hey Ewe!* on the dates applied for.
- Reproduce the lyrics to the songs on printed paper, such as for programmes, and to make transparencies for overhead projection. The following credit should be included: *'Reproduced by kind permission © Out of the Ark Ltd'.*
- Photocopy the script for learning purposes. Copies must be destroyed after the performance.
- Make no more than two copies of the music, to be used by participating musicians on the performance dates.

**If the performance is to be recorded please contact Out of the Ark Music.**

---

**We wish to apply for a licence to perform** *Hey Ewe!* **by Antony Copus**

**Customer number (if known):** ........................

**Name of school / organisation:** ....................................................................

**Name of organiser / producer:** ....................................................................

**Date(s) of performance(s):** ....................................................................

**Invoice address:** ....................................................................

....................................................................

**Post code:** ........................     **Country:** ..............................................

**Telephone number:** ....................................

---

| Number of performances (excl. dress rehearsal) | Performances without admission charges * | Performances with admission charges * |
|---|---|---|
| 1 | ☐ **£14.40** [€18.75] | ☐ **£19.20** [€25.00] |
| 2 | ☐ **£19.20** [€25.00] | ☐ **£24.00** [€31.20] |
| 3 or more | ☐ **£24.00** [€31.20] | ☐ **£30.13** [€39.20] |

Tick one of the boxes above.

☐ Tick here to receive licensing information for any audio or video recording of a performance.

---

**Tick one of the four payment options below:** (Invoices will be sent with all licences)

☐ Please bill my school/nursery at the above address (UK schools/nurseries only)

☐ I enclose a cheque (Pounds Sterling) for £ ......................... payable to Out of the Ark Music

☐ I enclose a cheque (Euro) for € ....................... payable to Out of the Ark Music

☐ Please charge the following card: (Visa [not Electron], MasterCard & Maestro accepted)

Card No ...............................................................................

Start Date _ _ / _ _ (MM/YY)     Expiry Date _ _ / _ _ (MM/YY)     3 digit security code: _ _ _ (last 3 digits on signature strip)

---

Address:   Out of the Ark Music         Phone:   +44 (0)20 8481 7200
           Kingsway Business Park        Fax:     +44 (0)20 8941 5548
           Oldfield Road                 Email:   info@outoftheark.com
           Hampton
           Middlesex  TW12 2HD
           United Kingdom

*The licence fees shown on this form are for 2013-2014 and include VAT at 20%. Prices may be subject to revision. Customers outside the EU will NOT be charged VAT.

# Christmas Musicals
## By Mark & Helen Johnson

### It's A Cracker!

A great new musical that mixes the Christmas dinner festivities with the awe and wonder of the Nativity story.
9 great songs that everyone will love.

• Age 5-9s
• Cast size: 25 upwards
• Speaking parts: 22
• Duration: c. 40 mins

### It's A Baby!

Told from the perspective of a weary innkeeper who finds he's in for a sleepless night, this natvity contains 9 songs and a simple script that can be easily extended. Wonderfully engaging and hugely entertaining!

• Age 3-7s
• Cast size: 12 upwards
• Speaking parts: minimum 3
• Duration: c. 30 mins

### It's A Party!

The invites were unusual... the guests were unlikely... and the venue was unconventional – but what a party! With 9 new songs, party on and celebrate in style with this brilliant nativity musical!

Age 5-9s •
Cast size: 24 upwards •
Speaking parts: minimum 16 •
Duration: c. 30 mins •

### Are We Nearly There Yet...?

Everyone is preparing to make the journey to Bethlehem.  Whilst Mary and Joseph, the shepherds and the angels set off, we join the Walker family on their journey.

• Age 5-9s
• Cast size: 18 upwards
• Speaking parts: minimum 18
• Duration: c. 35 mins

### Tinsel And Tea-Towels

Inc. enhanced CD with OHP lyrics, posters, tickets and much, much more!

This true-to-life and genuinely funny Christmas musical gives us a behind-the-scenes look at what happens when children in schools put on a nativity play.  Drawing on first-hand conversations with children, this musical helps us reflect on what the nativity story is all about.

• Age 5-9s
• Cast size: c. 50 (or whole school if you wish!)
• Speaking parts: 5 main & up to 50 with 1 or 2 lines each
• Duration: c. 40 mins

### Off To Bethlehem

9 delightful songs present the traditional Christmas story, without the need for lengthy narration or dialogue. Everything you need for a superb production is provided in this comprehensive package.

Age 5-9s •
Cast size: 21 upwards •
Duration: c. 30 mins •

## Each songbook package provides:

Quality recordings of all the songs, sung by children • Professionally arranged and produced backing tracks • Piano music with melody, lyrics and guitar chords • Photocopiable lyric sheets

**Out of the Ark Music** Kingsway Business Park, Oldfield Road, Hampton, Middlesex TW12 2HD,  UK
**Telephone:** +44 (0)20 8481 7200 **Fax:** +44 (0)20 8941 5548
**Email:** info@outoftheark.com  www.outoftheark.com

Out of the Ark Music